BLESSED
to be ME

Celebrate the Stories of your Life

A GUIDED JOURNAL

JEAN M. ALFIERI

BLESSED TO BE ME

www.BlessedtobeMe.com

Interior and Cover Design: Christine Sterling-Bortner
Original Artwork by Alexandra Ruiz
Quotes designed by Christine Sterling-Bortner

IBSN PRINT: 978-0-9991293-9-5

Celebrating the Stories of

Ready for an exciting and empowering journey?

"Blessed to be Me" is for people who have lived enough to know they have some kick-ass stories to tell! You appreciate what an extraordinary journey it's been, and it's not over. It is also for those who may not recognize all the blessings that have filled seemingly ordinary days. The real story is not about the number of years a person has lived, but about the life in those years.

This guided journal is about capturing the love, laughter and tears - all the many facets surrounding the life and times of YOU! Through the use of writing prompts and personal story-telling it will be easy to compile your top twelve (to-date) memories. Take a fresh look at YOU, and all the many things you are. With reflection, you can better appreciate how certain situations have unfolded. It also offers perspective not only on where you are now but also on everything that is still ahead. This is a focused project, designed to affirm and encourage.

The bonus of this book is that you are also creating a legacy. Tracking one's lineage can tell your family WHERE they came from. "Blessed to be Me" can reveal to loved ones WHO they came from! Are you a favorite grandma or the crazy aunt that everyone adores? The personal stories left untold by previous generations can be captured here for future generations to enjoy. Find hope and inspiration from the many blessings in your life, and then leave this book as a treasured keepsake to be passed along.

I wore many hats besides that of a writer when I created this journal. I was a career coach, a wife, a fur-mom, a real mom, just to name a few. But those titles did not completely define me. I'm also a person of love, peace, and gratitude. Still, I couldn't escape a grim period when I felt lost and unaccomplished. Had my life served any real purpose? I took an afternoon off to read and reflect on some essays I had written earlier in the year. These were a tribute of sorts, to special memories of certain people in my life. I began to see God's hand in the unfolding of those relationships, and how they were part of much bigger plans. What an awakening! Reflecting on the many blessings in my life lifted my spirits. It helped me realize that I had been looking inward instead of upward for strength.

Sharing some of these stories with my family sparked laughter, tears and fun conversations, as they recalled their versions of some of the events. These memories will forever hold a special place in our hearts.

I wouldn't provide you with a prompt that I'm not willing to tackle, so I've shared a few of my own stories at **www.BlessedtobeMe.com.** Along with some of my fondest memories and sad but pivotal God-sightings, you will find other resources to empower you on this writing journey. You too, are more than all the hats you wear. Let this book and website be the guides to compose the Stories of You, and you will then have a living heirloom to read, enjoy, and inspire. And if you choose, these special stories can be a lasting legacy for loved ones.

Each Blessing starts with positive affirmations to encourage you as you look forward to what lies ahead on your journey. It also includes a writing prompt, an outline of details, an inspiring quote, and a short section of Fun Facts or Flashback questions to capture even more memories. The tone, the texture and the spin are all yours.

Enjoy the look back at your real-life adventures! You may be surprised at what you discover. Forgotten treasures returning to warm your heart. A distant event examined from a new perspective. Whispered daydreams that became the foundation for later accomplishments. What else will you discover along the way? Let's find out!

YOUR BLESSINGS

How To (Best) Use This Book

Each writing segment will include prompts for the memories you choose to document. The tone, texture and spin are all you. Enjoy the look back at your real-life adventures!

<u>This book is for:</u>

- People with a life of stories that deserve telling
- Those in search of hope and inspiration
- Angels assisting loved ones to capture their life stories
- People wishing to create their own memoir to pass along
- Those who occasionally feel defeated
- Writers who need to change their perspective

<u>"Blessed to be Me" will:</u>

- Allow you to explore and reflect
- Prompt you to capture your fondest memories
- Guide you in composing a treasured keepsake
- Provide inspiration and encouragement on your journey ahead

As you consider the various topics in "Blessed to be Me," remember that these "favorite memories" don't have to be "happy"; nor do they have to be "sad" but they must be genuinely YOU, told only in a voice you can deliver. When you've completed each prompt, you will have captured twelve of your top (to-date) memories. You may be surprised at what you discover.

I learned my prompt-based true-life stories spanned many topics but none focused on my "major life accomplishments", such as graduating from college or getting my master's degree. Hitting those goals was memorable and important to my corporate career, but looking back, they didn't top out as my favorites. The ones I chose to write about were impactful on a different level. I encourage you to go deep, get personal with yourself, and most of all – have fun!

THE GIFT OF NO BOUNDARIES

You will find hints and suggestions offered with each Blessing. These are an assortment of ideas, from which you can pick and choose. Use what you like. Leave what you don't. This project is all about individual style. Let your personality shine!

"Blessed to be Me" is designed to be completed in any order you choose. You can compose each of your Blessings in order, or flip through the pages until you land on a special subject. You may choose to focus on the Affirmations within each chapter first, or vice-versa. You might ruminate and write one Blessing a month to complete your masterpiece in a year, or approach it on a more diligent schedule. Allow yourself permission to enjoy time with this study. Reflection is essential to the experience. Remember the saying: "Life is not about the destination, but the journey". Any way you approach it, you will produce a journal that captures the many different pieces of you.

If you are partnering to help someone capture his or her life story, you are truly an angel, providing a beautiful gift. Share the topic with the person a few days in advance of each session. This will allow your loved one time to decide which story to share and how to best tell it. Be gracious with your time and in seeking details. Memories may fade, which is why it's so special to capture them now!

Allow yourself grace. I believe that writing is a partnership with God. You are in a different place now than you were a decade ago, and will find yourself in a different place ten years from now. Consider your life journey in all its capacities: physically, emotionally, and spiritually. Perhaps this is a good time to be less critical and more embracing of yourself.

Look ahead with hope and courage. Why not trade in old thoughts that aren't serving you for new ones that will? Utilize the Powerful Ponderings offered with each challenge. Make your selection and write them on an index card. Tape them to your bathroom mirror (or other places) so you are reminded of them morning and night. Keep another copy in your purse, wallet or backpack, so you can review and repeat them every day. These positive affirmations are a powerful way to keep you on track and moving forward.

Blessing #1

It Must be Love

It seemed insignificant at the time. It was an ordinary day. Or perhaps it was an ordinary month, or year. You didn't notice what was playing out "behind the scenes." You didn't see how it was all unfolding according to God's great plan. But from this distance, now you can. How sweet it is!

Powerful Ponderings

Keeping your mind in focus with your intentions is key to achieving them. A powerful way of staying on track is through Affirmations. These positive thoughts empower you. Choose from the following or create your own! Write your selection on an index card and pin it up where you will see it, and/or keep it with you to reference throughout the day.

Choose your Affirmation for this topic:

- Today I will do more of what I love.
- I embrace this day with joy and happiness.
- I am thankful for all that today will be.
- My life is blessed with each new day.
- I appreciate and honor the flow of life.

(Repeat it daily and as you work on Blessing #1)

"You only live once, but if you do it right, once is enough."

– Mae West

Prompt #1 -How It All Started

Sometimes a story has begun before we even realize we're already in Chapter Two! Then, we need to trace it back to its origin. Sometimes an unlikely beginning is even mistaken for an ending. It's such fun to look back on a special relationship's humble (or not so humble) beginning. Every good story starts somewhere. Let's take this one from the top.

How did you meet one of the loves of your life?

On the following pages, write your story as you would tell it. Be sure you've included these key details:

- Where were you? (at school, playing sports, on the train)
- What time of year was it? (Date and time, if significant)
- Where did you live?
- What were you wearing?
- How did it happen?
- What did you say to each other?
- How did this person make you feel?
- When did you realize you were falling in love?

Fun Facts ☑

Who was your first date?

How old were you both?

Where did you go?

What did you do?

Blessing #2

A New Beginning

It was a new beginning. A big decision. A day you decided to put in to action what you'd been dreaming about. And the start of something beautiful.

If we open our hearts to God's purpose for us, we will likely be surprised to see that what He has planned is so much greater than any plans we could make for ourselves. Find comfort in this and know the Lord will guide your steps. Ask him at the start of each day to lead you. Be thankful for His love and patience.

POWERFUL PONDERINGS

Time to trade in those old thoughts that aren't serving you for new ones that will! A powerful way of staying focused on your goal is through Affirmations. These positive thoughts empower you. Which of the following resonates with you? Write your selection on an index card and pin it up where you will see it, and/or keep it with you to reference throughout the day.

Choose your Affirmation for this topic:

- I clearly see the blessings that surround me.
- My heart is open to my new beginning.
- Positive changes are happening. I welcome and embrace them.
- I say "Yes" to new adventures.
- The best time for a new beginning is now.

(Repeat it daily and as you work on Blessing #2)

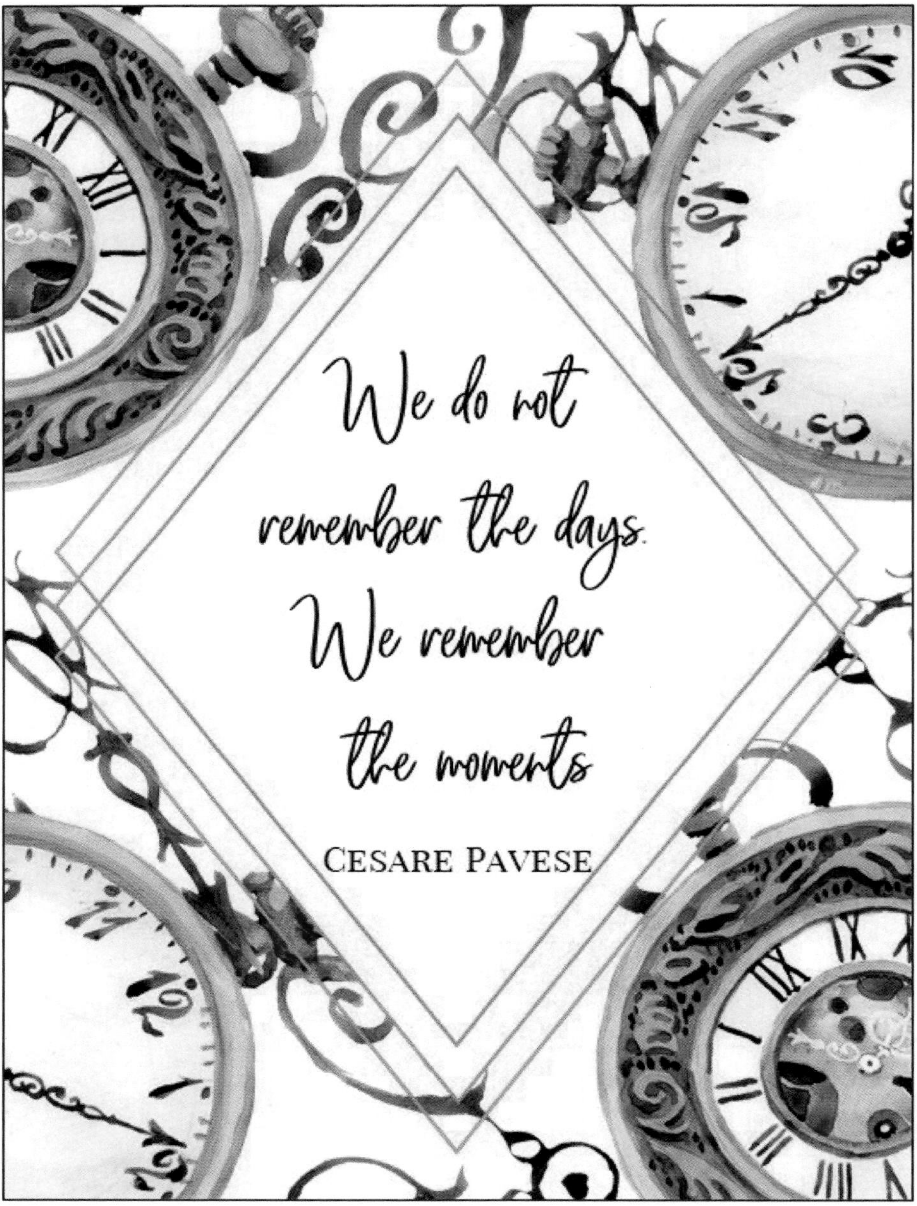
We do not
remember the days.
We remember
the moments
CESARE PAVESE

Prompt #2 - The Time Had Come

There's something undeniably exciting about a countdown. You stand on the threshold of walking down the aisle. You close the doors of the moving van and begin the drive to your new life in a new place. You finish packing the kid's suitcases for Disneyland!

What was it for you?

- The start of a New Year
- The first day of a new job
- A move to a new city
- Putting a plan into action
- Your wedding day
- Watching a space launch
- Diving in (literally or figuratively)

Remember to include these key elements:

- How did you plan for it?
- Did it happen as you planned it?
- What was the best part?

FLASHBACK

WHAT ADVICE YOU WOULD OFFER A "YOUNGER-YOU" BASED ON THE SHORT STORY YOU CREATED FROM THIS PROMPT?

Blessing #3

Finding Clarity

It is not always easy to find our path, let alone, to stay on it. We may find ourselves caught up in regret or left wondering where we took the wrong turn. Often, we must walk in faith. Remember that the Lord is with you. Ask him to guide each step. Lean on him in times of trial or darkness. Pray each day for his guidance over all that you think, that you say, and that you do. And rest well, knowing He provides peace and joy.

Powerful Ponderings

Keeping your mind in focus with your intentions is key to achieving them. A powerful way of staying on track is through Affirmations. These positive thoughts empower you. Choose from the following or create your own! Write your selection on an index card and pin it up where you will see it, and/or keep it with you to reference throughout the day.

Choose your Affirmation for this topic:

- I see my dreams clearly and I claim them.
- I choose to follow my own unique and true purpose.
- My life is well-balanced, and my vision is focused.
- I appreciate and am present in this day.
- I see the world clearly and live my life with purpose.

(Repeat it daily and as you work on Blessing #3)

Life is grand. Love is real. And beauty is everywhere.

–SONG LYRIC FROM "BETTER BEAUTIFUL THAN PERFECT" BY ROGER CLYNE & THE PEACEMAKERS

PROMPT #3 - I CAN SEE CLEARLY NOW

Sometimes, when the fog lifts, all that preceded it, is suddenly obvious. Your eyes are opened. Other times, it leaves you reeling as you try to piece it all together.

Write about a time that you became aware of a situation for what it really was, and not what you had mistakenly thought it was. Be sure to include:

- What was blocking your vision?
- Was it a literal fog, as you tried to drive somewhere? Or a mental fog that clouded your thoughts?
- When did it clear?
- Was anyone there to help you?
- Did you seek assistance?
- What did you do?
- How did you feel?
- How was it resolved?
- How are you different now as a result of it?

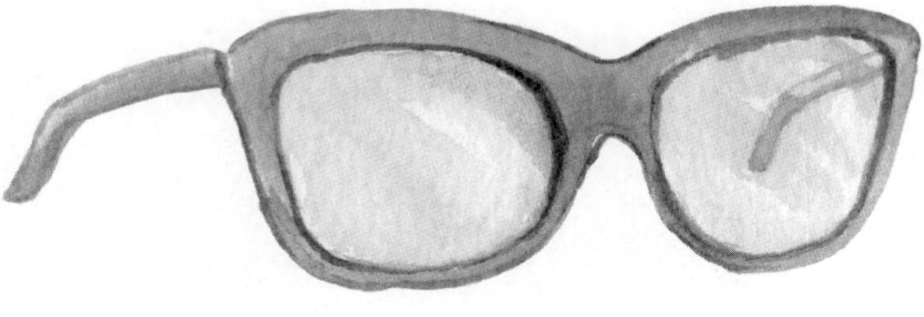

Fun Facts ☑

What were your favorite songs growing up?

Title / Artist

Who are your favorite bands?

What was your first concert?

- When was it?
- Where was it?
- Who did you go with?
- How did you get there?

Tomatoes and oregano make it Italian; wine and Tarragon make it French; sour cream makes it Russian; lemon and cinnamon make it Greek; soy sauce makes it Chinese; garlic makes it good.
Alice May Brock

Blessing #4

Live, Love, Laugh

It seems the more we live and the more we love, the more we laugh. It all goes hand-in-hand so beautifully. Laughter is like music to God's ears. It has the power to heal your soul. Never underestimate the power a smile can bring – from you, and to you. Wear it well!

POWERFUL PONDERINGS

Time to trade in those old thoughts that aren't serving you for new ones that will! A powerful way of staying focused on your goal is through Affirmations. These positive thoughts empower you. Which of the following resonates with you? Write your selection on an index card and pin it up where you will see it, and/or keep it with you to reference throughout the day.

Choose your Affirmation for this topic:

- My life is full of love, laughter, and abundance.
- I love laughter. It heals my soul.
- When I laugh I feel light and happy.
- When I laugh I release all negative vibes.
- With my smile I create positive energy.

(Repeat it daily and as you work on Blessing #4)

Laughter is
an instant
Vacation

MILTON
BERLE

PROMPT #4 - NOW THAT WAS FUNNY!

It's true that smiles are contagious. Timing is everything. Isn't it great when someone tells a joke with perfect delivery? Or your pet does something quirky and cute and you look just in time to catch it?

When was the last time something or someone unexpectedly made you laugh out loud? I hope you don't have to think back too far! Or, a time you tried not to laugh, but couldn't contain it. You know how that goes. The more you try to stop, the worse it gets!

Laughter is such a joy! Why don't we do it more often? The health benefits are numerous, and it just feels good. The louder the better! (Did you just snort?!)

What funny story do you LOVE to retell? Write it just as you would tell it. Then make sure you've included these details:

- What was so funny?
- Who made you laugh?
- Did anyone snort or fart?
- Why did it tickle your funny bone?
- When you retell this story, does it still make you laugh?

Flashback

What favorite game did you play in your youth?

Who was your first best friend?

How did you meet?

Who and what was your first family pet?

What did you enjoy doing on the weekends?

Blessing #5

This is Important

It's the foundation of who you are. You believe in it because you've been exposed to it and submerged in it. You live it every day and you know it's right. You are never happier than when you are in some way associated or involved in it. You love it!

POWERFUL PONDERINGS

Keeping your mind in focus with your intentions is key to achieving them. A powerful way of staying on track is through Affirmations. These positive thoughts empower you. Choose from the following or create your own! Write your selection on an index card and pin it up where you will see it, and/or keep it with you to reference throughout the day.

Choose your Affirmation for this topic:

- I am aligned with my mission in life.
- I take action and move confidently toward my life purpose.
- Making a difference – that's what I do.
- I am committed to being my best self each day.
- Following my purpose is easy for me.

(Repeat it daily and as you work on Blessing #5)

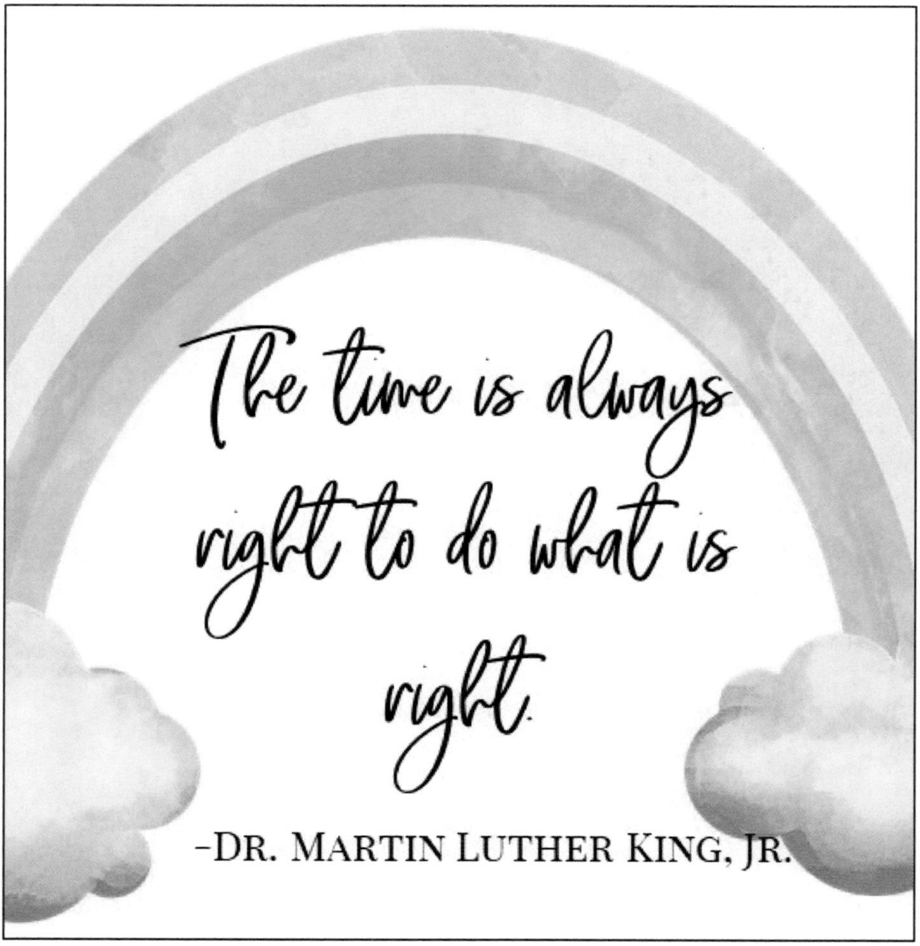
The time is always right to do what is right.
-Dr. Martin Luther King, Jr.

PROMPT #5 - YOUR TESTIMONIAL

It's the thing that you are most passionate about. It's the reason you get out of bed in the morning. It stirs something within you. You talk about it, promote it and support it.

You may have multiple causes to which you are dedicated. If so, you may want to pick your Top One. Or you may want to expand this section and create multiple testimonials.

Write your testimonial about that which you believe in so deeply and have unselfishly dedicated time and energy to support. Consider these questions:

- What are you passionate about?
- To what cause do you contribute or volunteer your time?
- Why should others share your concern or be interested?
- How can people get involved or support it?
- Tell your story. Share the reason for your commitment.

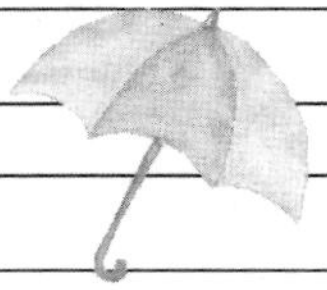

HERE AND NOW

WHAT MAKES YOU HAPPIEST ABOUT THE SUBJECT OF YOUR TESTIMONIAL?

Love is the flower you've
got to let grow.
- John Lennon

Blessing #6

WHAT INSPIRES YOU?

It may be something powerful and miraculous, or as simple as your favorite cup of coffee. It lifts your spirits and touches your heart. You are encouraged whenever you see it. It gives you energy and hope. Sharing it makes your soul dance. You have a special peace and confidence deep down inside when you connect to it. What is that special something?

Powerful Ponderings

Time to trade in those old thoughts that aren't serving you for new ones that will! A powerful way of staying focused on your goal is through Affirmations. These positive thoughts empower you. Which of the following resonates with you? Write your selection on an index card and pin it up where you will see it, and/or keep it with you to reference throughout the day.

Choose your Affirmation for this topic:

- I live a hopeful, loving, and inspired life.
- I give up what no longer serves me and fill that space with confidence.
- I trust God to provide all I need in this day.
- I am inspired to move courageously through each day.
- I believe life is unfolding just as it should.

(Repeat it daily and as you work on Blessing #6)

A little magic can take you a long way.

-FROM JAMES AND THE GIANT PEACH, BY ROALD DAHL

Prompt #6 - It's the Little Things

Here's to the places, people and things that carry a special inspiration! Perhaps you went somewhere for the purpose of being inspired. Or maybe finding inspiration by what you encountered took you by surprise.

- Is there a special "sign" that inspires you (like a rainbow)?
- Is it receiving a smile or a hug?
- Has there ever been an act of kindness that you witnessed which prompted you do something similar?
- Is there a certain aspect of nature that inspires (a sunrise, a flower, a bird)?
- What action are you prompted to take when you become inspired?
- How does that make you feel?
- What do you do to seek it out when you feel uninspired?

FLASHBACK

DID YOUR FAMILY OR FRIENDS EVER GIVE YOU A NICKNAME?

WHO IN YOUR CIRCLE OF FRIENDS HAD A NICKNAME THAT WAS WELL-SUITED FOR THEM?

Blessing #7

A MOMENT IN TIME

You know what it's like to experience the peaks and valleys. Some of the valleys felt so low that to emerge, you had to dig yourself out from a pit. Some of the highs were so soaring, that you felt as if you could fly. Then there were those other times, that almost defy description.

Maybe it was those late-teen years, when you went away and got lost (or found) on a large University campus, attended a local community college, or ditched the route of higher education, and secured your first real job.

Maybe it was the impact of the pandemic called the Coronavirus. Was this the most unusual situation and human behavior you've experienced? Or do you have an even more intriguing tale to tell? These extraordinary times created the foundation for everything that followed, and guaranteed some memorable stories.

POWERFUL PONDERINGS

Keeping your mind in focus with your intentions is key to achieving them. A powerful way of staying on track is through Affirmations. These positive thoughts empower you. Choose from the following or create your own! Write your selection on an index card and pin it up where you will see it, and/or keep it with you to reference throughout the day.

Choose your Affirmation for this topic:

- I choose peace, love and joy and am content in this moment.
- I am surrounded by love and light.
- I am living a bright and abundant life.
- I freely give and receive love, peace, and happiness.
- I spread happiness and joy where ever I go.

(Repeat it daily and as you work on Blessing #7)

Nobody told me there'd be days like these. Strange days, indeed.

– SONG LYRIC FROM "NOBODY TOLD ME" BY JOHN LENNON

PROMPT # 7 -THE BEST, THE WORST, AND THE WEIRDEST OF DAYS

What do you consider your "best" times to date? Was it a relationship, a series of years or a particular decade?

What is the "worst" time you've endured, and how did you get through it? This story is important to recalling your strengths and to encourage others who might walk a similar path.

What were your "weirdest" of times? These were strange days, and what transpired influenced the rest of your life. How did they shape the person you are today?

BEST OF TIMES:

WORST OF TIMES:

WEIRDEST OF TIMES:

FLASHBACK

WHO WERE YOUR BEST FRIENDS IN HIGH SCHOOL AND/OR COLLEGE?

WHICH OF THOSE FRIENDSHIPS HAVE ENDURED THROUGH THE YEARS?

WHAT WAS THE BEST ADVICE YOU RECEIVED? WHO GAVE IT TO YOU?

Blessing #8

Along with You

Who has God given you to be along for this ride? Don't underestimate their importance. You were put here in this place, at this time, for a reason, and so were they. We are surrounded by loving and supportive people. Whether a family member, a dear friend, or a recent acquaintance, we are blessed by their presence and the encouragement they share.

POWERFUL PONDERINGS

Time to trade in those old thoughts that aren't serving you for new ones that will! A powerful way of staying focused on your goal is through Affirmations. These positive thoughts empower you. Which of the following resonates with you? Write your selection on an index card and pin it up where you will see it, and/or keep it with you to reference throughout the day.

Choose your Affirmation for this topic:

- I am thankful for those that God has graciously provided in my life.
- I delight in the simple pleasures of life.
- God provides the love and support I need right now.
- I am thankful for the blessing of friends in my life.
- I open my heart to the joyfulness of this day.

(Repeat it daily and as you work on Blessing #8)

God is busy making you someone no one else has ever been

– BETH MOORE

PROMPT #8 - INTERVIEW EXCHANGE

This is a special opportunity to not only learn why those closest to you love and cherish you in their life but to give back to them! Tell them what you treasure most about your relationship. This questionnaire can be the foundation for a great exchange with a long-time friend or sibling.

Review the questionnaire. Think of a close friend; one who has seen you through good times and bad. One with whom you've shared fond memories.

Ask for 30 minutes of their time. Offer to either interview him/her directly, over the phone or in person. Or, they can opt to type up their responses and email to you.

Email them the questions in advance of your meeting or agreed upon exchange date, so they have a chance to compose their answers. (You will have done the same.)

Interview Questions

1. We have been friends since ______ (this might be an actual year, or place, or school grade, or event/point in time)

2. If someone asked me to describe you, I'd say:

3. One of the best times we had was ...

4. I still laugh when I think about ....

5. I WAS SO PROUD OF YOU WHEN ...

6. WHAT I ADMIRE MOST ABOUT YOU:

7. I TREASURE OUR FRIENDSHIP BECAUSE ...

HERE AND NOW

WHAT 3 THINGS ARE YOU MOST THANKFUL FOR TODAY?

Blessing #9

SOMEONE SPECIAL

Sometimes we're not even aware that we've met someone who will walk beside us down all of life's winding roads. Other times a person shows up for just a brief while, but makes such an impact that they leave an unforgettable treasure of memories in their wake. Your heart is happier and your life is fuller when this person is around. With this special someone, you've had an unforgettable time!

POWERFUL PONDERINGS

Keeping your mind in focus with your intentions is key to achieving them. A powerful way of staying on track is through Affirmations. These positive thoughts empower you. Choose from the following or create your own! Write your selection on an index card and pin it up where you will see it, and/or keep it with you to reference throughout the day.

Choose your Affirmation for this topic:

- I embrace and enjoy the simple things in life.
- I surround myself with supportive and loving friends.
- I find beauty and happiness in ordinary moments.
- I pray for myself and for my friends this day.
- I am thankful for this day and all that it will be.

(Repeat it daily and as you work on Blessing #9)

If you obey all the rules, you miss all the fun.
– Katherine Hepburn

Prompt # 9 - Remember That Time?

It was a fabulous time! It could never be replicated. When you think about this story, it always makes you smile. Maybe some even doubt it's true!

- Who was your accomplice? A friend, a sibling, a co-worker?
- Where were you?
- When was it? (time of year/ time of day)
- How old were you?
- How did it start?
- What happened that was so memorable?
- How did it end?

FLASHBACK

WHAT WAS ONE OF YOUR MOST MEMORABLE SUMMER JOBS?

WHERE WOULD ALL YOUR FRIENDS MEET TO HANG-OUT?

Blessing #10

The Time to Save. A Time to Splurge.

When my dog looks at me with her big brown eyes, shamelessly begging for a treat, I know what she is thinking: “Why say No, when saying Yes feels so good?!” Sometimes life calls for discretion. Other times, not so much! When have you known in your gut that something was right, so you planned and budgeted for it? - Or, blew the budget and just went for it?!

Powerful Ponderings

Time to trade in those old thoughts that aren’t serving you for new ones that will! A powerful way of staying focused on your goal is through Affirmations. These positive thoughts empower you. Which of the following resonates with you? Write your selection on an index card and pin it up where you will see it, and/or keep it with you to reference throughout the day.

Choose your Affirmation for this topic:

- I give up what no longer serves me and fill that space with confidence.
- I trust God to provide all I need in this day.
- I move confidently and courageously through each day.
- I believe life is unfolding just as it should.
- I will do what I can and leave the rest in God’s mighty hands.

(Repeat it daily and as you work on Blessing #10)

Life is either a daring adventure or nothing.

–Helen Keller

PROMPT # 10 - BEST VACATION EVER!

Maybe it was on your bucket list. Or perhaps you simply accepted an invitation. It may have been a "stay-cation" in your own backyard. Regardless of whether you expected it to be so memorable or not, you had the best time ever! Isn't it wonderful to escape the routine and experience something new?

Perhaps there's more than one favorite to share! If so, make a list and include 2-3 sentences explaining why each was unforgettable.

There are so many ways to get-away: a family vacation, Honeymoon, a reunion, a private retreat.

- What was your best vacation to date?
- How was it planned?
- What was your route?
- How did you get there?
- Who accompanied you?
- What was the best part?

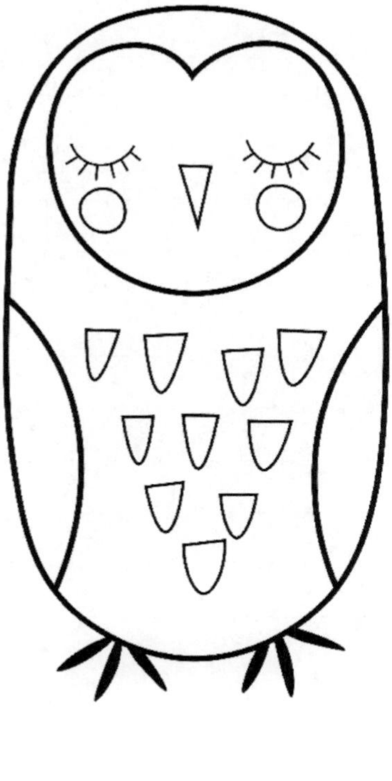

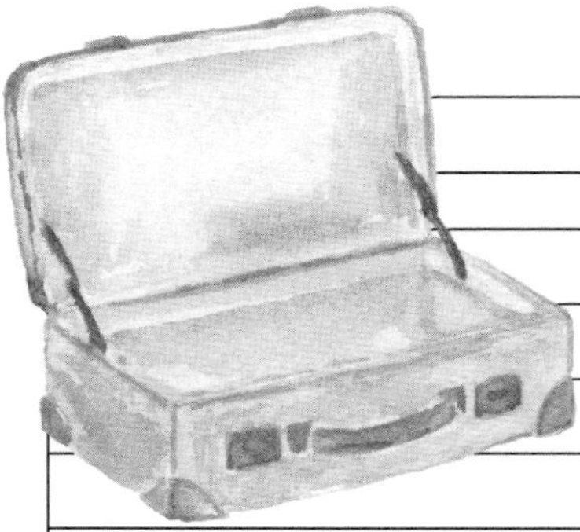

FUN FACTS ☑

WHAT WAS THE FIRST VEHICLE YOU WERE ALLOWED TO DRIVE?

WHAT WAS THE FIRST VEHICLE YOU OWNED?

WHAT HAS ALWAYS BEEN YOUR DREAM VEHICLE?

There is no blue without yellow and without orange.
- Vincent Van Gogh

Blessing #11

In His Presence

Sometimes we think of God as operating only in extraordinary ways. It's harder to see him in our ordinary everyday lives. With a universe to attend to, He looks for us, appoints us, and works through us in ways we may not recognize ... until sometime later. We can't always see the happy ending from the miserable middle chapter that we feel stuck in. But sometimes we can get a glimpse of God's miraculous work.

POWERFUL PONDERINGS

Keeping your mind in focus with your intentions is key to achieving them. A powerful way of staying on track is through Affirmations. These positive thoughts empower you. Choose from the following or create your own! Write your selection on an index card and pin it up where you will see it, and/or keep it with you to reference throughout the day.

Choose your Affirmation for this topic:

- I live every day connected to Spirit and living my higher purpose.
- The holy spirit is working through me every day.
- Throughout this day I ask the Lord to guide my every step.
- I pray that God will guide all I think, say and do.
- I am surrounded by God's love and grace.

(Repeat it daily and as you work on Blessing #11)

It is in facing our need that we find God's great supply.
-ALISTAIR BEGG

PROMPT # 11 - A "GOD SIGHTING"

"God-sightings" are all around us. In a brilliant sunset, or a double rainbow. Sometimes we can feel his presence in our deepest time of need. Angels surround us. Sometimes so closely, it seems like we could reach out and touch them. And sometimes we do, like when a friend shows up unexpectedly when we've just received bad news. Or a stranger helps out when you least expect but most need it. In what special way have you encountered God?

- Where were you?
- Were you alone or with someone?
- What happened?
- How was it significant? - Was it incredible? An answer to prayers?
- What did you feel or say?
- What did you take away from this experience?

Here and Now

What insights have you gained (what life lesson have you learned) that you would share with others?

I AM LEARNING
TO BE GRATEFUL EACH DAY

Blessing #12

LET'S FACE IT

They say what doesn't kill you, makes you stronger. I'm not sure about that, but prayer can make us stronger. We all tackle our problems differently. The key is to tackle them! When something becomes a roadblock, we have to acknowledge it and find our way around, over, or straight through it. What have you been triumphant in overcoming?

POWERFUL PONDERINGS

Time to trade in those old thoughts that aren't serving you for new ones that will! A powerful way of staying focused on your goal is through Affirmations. These positive thoughts empower you. Which of the following resonates with you? Write your selection on an index card and pin it up where you will see it, and/or keep it with you to reference throughout the day.

Choose your Affirmation for this topic:

- I have all the resources I need to make this a successful day.
- I am fully equipped and prepared to take on all today will offer.
- No one can live my life better than me.
- I am blessed to take on the challenges of today.
- I face today with gratitude, love, and hopefulness.

(Repeat it daily and as you work on Blessing #12)

The two most
important
days of your
life are the day you
were born, and the day
you find out why.

–Mark Twain

PROMPT # 12 - PROMPT: FACING _____

We all face something. This can be a reflective commentary on a significant life-event or a forward pondering on what such an event may look like when you get there. Share with God what's on your heart. What is your game plan? Don't just define the challenge, solve it! And be sure to come back and record how you conquered it!

- What did you face? - Adversity, hitting a certain age, an illness, a person, your greatest fear?
- Why was it significant?
- What was the most difficult thing about it?
- Who did you tell about it?
- When did you first realize you had to face it?
- How did you approach it?
- What did you do?
- How did it turn out?

HERE AND NOW

List 3 things that you are grateful for this week, and the reasons why.

Congratulations

YOU DID IT!

Here Are Two Bonus Blessings!

Bonus Blessing #1

AN AWESOME FAMILY STORY

This story may not even include you, but you've heard it repeated many times. Or perhaps it's a story about you but you were too young to remember when it happened. It may be your grandparents who love telling it most, but everybody knows it. It's a classic!

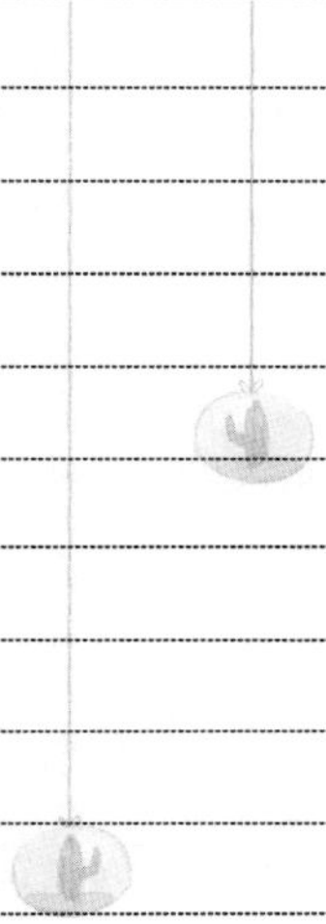

Bonus Flashback

What has been your most special Birthday celebration to date?

Was it a milestone birthday on which you did something extra special?

Was it one in which someone surprised you?

Was it one in which you went out or hosted a party? Do you have any pictures of it?

A smile is a curve that sets everything straight.

– Phyllis Diller

Bonus Blessing #2

Photo Captions

I love Instagram. I agree that a picture can tell a thousand words. But when I learned that very few viewers actually read the captions, I decided I wouldn't include the whole backstory, but just a sentence or two. This is a great practice for Twitter as well.

OPTION 1: Review your phone's photo gallery. Pick 5 unrelated pictures and give them a 1-3 sentence caption. You do not have to describe what the pictures are about. Instead, capture how the pictures makes you feel. Or, express what the person, pet, tree, or flower might be thinking (in their own words). It may be sweet and sensitive, or silly and humorous.

OPTION 2: Pictures of YOU. Go back to a yearbook from school or a family scrapbook. Find pictures of you and your friends. How would you caption them now in just 1-3 sentences? If you put a dialogue-bubble over your heads, what would it reveal you were thinking?

DOES THIS EXERCISE "PROMPT" ANY LONGER STORIES?

There are no bad pictures; that's just how your face looks sometimes.

– ABRAHAM LINCOLN

The Bucket List

What great adventures are on your horizon? Exploring a new culture, climbing a volcano, or perhaps learning to paint? Dream big. It may just be your next best memory!

About the Author

Jean knew when her eyes locked with those of a smooshy-faced little dog who sat inside a kennel at the Humane Society, that it was love at first sight. She was compelled to self-published a collection of short story poems starring her often mischievous and always adorable rescue pug named Zuggy some years later, after he passed away. Saddened by the prospect that her fondest memories with her beloved pet might be forgotten, Jean realized how much of our human legacy is lost within a single generation. Inspired, she created “Blessed to be Me”, a way of capturing and celebrating the stories of your life. Now Jean encourages others to share their amazing stories in this guided journal.

The book as well as the **BlessedtobeMe.com** website provide tips and resources, all the simple tools you need to move forward. Jean also offers presentations and keynotes on the subject and enjoys visiting groups to offer others inspiration and support on their exciting and life-changing writing journey.

Jean is a veteran of Human Resources and Organizational Development in both small and large companies, where she served 28 years in the field. She taught undergraduate HR classes and the HR certification preparatory classes. She decided to step out from the corporate world to fulfill her own personal goals. She now splits her time between coaching, writing, and volunteering at her local Humane Society.

Acknowledgments

First, I thank our LORD, who I pray to for guidance in all that I think, say, do, and write; and who faithfully leads me through every day. I love how the right people show up and situations play out for HIS purpose and that HE has allowed me glimpses of this as I look back on my life. It gives me courage to look forward, knowing with HIM, I will always be blessed.

Thanks to DEBBY ENGLANDER and her web workshop: Bionic Book Writing. To all the coaches and resources offered by STEVE HARRISON'S Quantum Leap program. Such a treasure-trove of wisdom!

Thanks to CHRISTINE STERLING-BORTNER for taking on the challenge of self-publishing coach and print lay-out/design extraordinaire. It truly does take a village and you are a one-stop shop!

Thanks to DIANE CAMPBELL and the ACFW critique group who, with much love and patience, offer constructive feedback and inspiration. To KAREN BARTA-BAIRD, who blesses me in many ways, and most recently, with her proofreading skills. And to CAROL CUPPY, for your uplifting perspective, critical eye and fresh ideas, all served best over a cup of coffee.

Special thanks to the social media gurus who help all of us improve our on-line presence:

SEAN CANNEL – I'm not yet crushing it, but me and the pug are sure having fun creating our semi-serious but mostly silly videos for Zuggy Pug's YouTube channel!

PAT FLYNN – I have so much to learn from you. I can't wait to Podcast.

CHELENE JOHNSON – I discovered you through Turbo-Jam and you continued to motivate me. Thank you for your "Do it now!" attitude.

Last but never least, to my husband JOSH – for your encouragement and support. You are the love of my life and my biggest blessing. (I would never sell you to the circus!)